CHESTER'S EASIE

ANIMAL TUNES

Written and arranged by Carol Barratt

For Andra and Karoline Zobens East

Illustrated by Sarah Lenton

Chester Music Limited
(A division of Music Sales Limited)
8/9 Frith Street, London W1V 5TZ.

This book © Copyright 1996 Chester Music.
Order No. CH61105 ISBN 0-7119-5610-3

Visit the Music Sales Internet Music Shop at
http://www.musicsales.co.uk

Illustrations by Sarah Lenton
© 1996 Sarah Lenton.

Music processed by Barnes Music Engraving.
Printed in the United Kingdom by Caligraving Limited, Thetford, Norfolk.

THE PONY

Felix Le Couppey (1811-1887)

THE CUCKOO

August Eberhard Müller (1767–1817)

THE ELEPHANT

From *The Carnival of the Animals*

Camille Saint-Saëns (1835–1921)

Allegretto pomposo

THE BEAR

Dmitri Shostakovich (1906–1975)
(Edited by Carol Barratt)

Allegretto

8ve

THE CAT IN THE CORNER

Irish Fiddle Tune

AUNTY LIZZIE'S OLD PIG

Carol Barratt

THE CROW

This tune uses the Pentatonic Scale (5 note scale)
which starting on C is:

Chinese Folk Tune

THE CAT

From *Peter and the Wolf*

Sergei Prokofieff (1891–1953)

SWAN LAKE

Peter Ilich Tchaikovsky (1840–1893)

THE DUCK

From *Peter and the Wolf*

Sergei Prokofieff (1891–1953)

SHEEP MAY SAFELY GRAZE

Johann Sebastian Bach (1685–1750)

GIRAFFES

Carol Barratt

Slowly and gracefully